QUIVER
PART 1

Eaglemoss Ltd. 2015
1st Floor, Kensington Village, Avonmore Road,
W14 8TS, London, UK.
All rights reserved.

Editorial Director: Maggie Calmels
Editorial Managers: Richard Jackson, Ben Robinson
Editor: Will Potter
Book Design: Steve Scanlan
Introductions: James Hill

OUR COLLECTION
DC Comics Graphic Novel Collection is published fortnightly.

DON'T MISS AN ISSUE: place a regular order with your
magazine retailer.

SUBSCRIBE and receive exclusive free gifts!
To subscribe: Visit our website at www.eaglemoss.com/dc-books
Call our hotline 0371 277 0112
Post the subscription form (which you will find inside issues
1, 2, 3, 4 & 5)

BACK ISSUES
To order back issues:
Order online at www.eaglemoss.com/dc-books
or call 0371 277 0112

UK distributor: COMAG Magazine Marketing

UK CUSTOMER SERVICES
Call: 0371 277 0112
Email: dc-books@eaglemoss.service.com
Write to: DC Comics Graphic Novel Collection, Database Factory,
Unit 4, Pullman Business Park, Pullman Way, Ringwood, Hampshire,
BH24 1HD

Australia
Call: (03) 9872 4000
E-mail: bissett@bissettmags.com.au
Write to: DC Comics Graphic Novel Collection,
Bissett Magazine
Service Pty Limited,
PO Box 3460 Nunawading, VIC 3131

South Africa
Call: (011) 265 4307
E-mail: service@jacklin.co.za
Write to: DC Comics Graphic Novel Collection,
Eaglemoss Ltd,
Private Bag 18, Centurion 0046

OVERSEAS BACK ISSUES
Place your order with your local magazine retailer.

Visit our website: www.eaglemoss.com/dc-books

QUIVER
PART 1

KEVIN SMITH
WRITER

PHIL HESTER
PENCILLER

ANDE PARKS
INKER

SEAN KONOT
LETTERER

GUY MAJOR
COLOURIST

THE BRAVE AND THE BOLD #85
BOB HANEY
WRITER

NEAL ADAMS
PENCILLER

DICK GIORDANO
INKER

Bob Schreck Editor – Original Series
Michael Wright Associate Editor – Original Series
Nachie Castro Assistant Editor – Original Series
Murray Boltinoff Editor – *The Brave and the Bold* #85
Nick J. Napolitano Editor – Collected Edition
Scott Nybakken Associate Editor – Collected Edition

INTRODUCING...
QUIVER

Green Arrow: Quiver returned Oliver Queen to the DC Universe. Penned by Kevin Smith, a longtime comic book fan and independent filmmaker, the book paid homage to all that had gone before while simultaneously stripping off the creative barnacles to position Green Arrow as a hero fit for the new millennium.

For much of the 1980s and 1990s, Oliver Queen had operated as a solo vigilante, his interactions with the wider DC Universe largely confined to team ups with non-powered heroes such as Batman and the Question. In *Green Arrow* #100-101 (September-October 1995), Oliver Queen was killed in action, his heroic legacy passing on to his son, Connor Hawke.

Rather than simply ignoring these dramatic changes, Smith worked them into his narrative. He cleverly resurrected Oliver Queen as a man literally from another time, the changes in the DC Universe as bewildering to the reborn hero as they were to some readers. *Green Arrow: Quiver* also drew on continuity from the wider DC Universe. It featured cameo appearances from many fan-favourite characters, using supernatural characters to great effect, and it even pulled in elements from Neil Gaiman's epic *Sandman*. At the end of the book, Oliver Queen was anything but a solo operative. He was once again a major player at the heart of an expansive mythos.

Renowned for his skill with dialogue, Smith was ably assisted by artists Phil Hester and Ande Parks, who captured every emotional nuance with expressive character work. While the book was filled with sparkling dialogue, Smith also knew when to simply get out of the way and let Hester and Parks' explosive art shine, as witnessed by the cliffhanger introduction of Etrigan the Demon in this volume.

KEVIN SMITH is an award-winning independent filmmaker, perhaps best known for movies set within the 'View Askewniverse', such as *Clerks*, *Chasing Amy* and *Dogma*. A lifelong comic fan, Smith sold his treasured comic book collection to help finance his first movie. He has since written numerous best-selling comics, including *Daredevil: Guardian Devil* and *Spider-Man/Black Cat: The Evil That Men Do* for Marvel and BATMAN: CACOPHONY and BATMAN '66 MEETS THE GREEN HORNET for DC Comics. Smith produces, and occasionally appears in, the reality television series *Comic Book Men*, which is set within Smith's own comic book shop, Jay and Silent Bob's Secret Stash. Smith's SModcast.com is a potpourri of pop culture punditry and opinion.

PHIL HESTER is an Eisner Award-nominated artist/writer who was born in eastern Iowa, USA. He entered the comic book industry while still attending classes at the University of Iowa and has since

BIOGRAPHIES

worked for every major publisher in the field. His pencilling credits include SWAMP THING, NIGHTWING and THE FLASH: SEASON ZERO for DC Comics and *The Irredeemable Ant-Man* and *Ultimate Marvel Team-Up* for Marvel. Hester has written numerous comic book series, including the cult classic *Green Hornet* and, in conjunction with Kevin Smith, a reworking of *The Bionic Man*, both published by Dynamite Entertainment.

ANDE PARKS was born and raised in Kansas and began his professional comic book career inking such titles as WONDER WOMAN, GREEN ARROW and NIGHTWING, often teamed with his longtime friend penciller Phil Hester. As much a writer as an artist, Parks drew on local history to pen *Union Station*, a graphic novel that dealt with events surrounding the notorious 1933 Kansas City massacre, which was published in 2004 by Oni Press. He returned to the genre of historical fiction the following year to produce *Capote in Kansas*, a graphic biography drawn by Chris Samnee. Parks has also written *Kato*, *Lone Ranger* and other titles for Dynamite Entertainment.

THE STORY SO FAR...

While on a south sea cruise, a corrupt business partner betrayed billionaire Oliver Queen and knocked him overboard. Queen washed up on a remote island, where he fashioned a crude bow and arrow, which he used to take down a drug-running operation controlled by the villain China White. Back home in Star City, Queen continued to use his bow to great effect as the super hero Green Arrow. He adopted Roy Harper as his crime-fighting sidekick, Speedy, and secretly used his wealth to bankroll the Justice League of America, before going on to join the group.

While serving as member of the JLA, Green Arrow met and fell in love with Black Canary. Despite finding happiness in his personal life, Green Arrow grew disillusioned with the JLA's global focus, feeling that his fellow heroes had lost touch with the common people. After being swindled out of his fortune by financier John DeLeon, Green Arrow took a road trip with Black Canary and Green Lantern Hal Jordan to explore the heartland of America.

Green Arrow eventually left the JLA and moved to Seattle with Black Canary, although their romance hit the rocks, due largely to Oliver's increasingly obsessive behaviour. Tensions between the former lovers reached breaking point following the revelation that Oliver had sired an illegitimate son, Connor Hawke, some years earlier.

While attempting to prevent terrorists from triggering a bomb over the city of Metropolis, Green Arrow willingly sacrificed himself to save the lives of millions. Following the heroic death of Oliver Queen, Connor Hawke continued his father's crime-fighting legacy as the second Green Arrow.

CHAPTER ONE:
THE QUEEN IS
DEAD
Long Live the Queen!

NEW YORK CITY.

THE PRESENT.

Put the kibosh on the transaction as physically as you can without taking a life or getting perforated by the N.R.A.-sanctioned automatic weapons and win the game.

Great.

Heroin.

It always has to be heroin.

The waiting game.

Milton Bradley oughta market this one.

For ages 'kid sidekick' and up. Any number can play. Sit still for hours, waiting for some Tony Montana-wannabe to score a king's ransom in horse from the local smack-peddler.

Not that it affects the wait, anyway. Hell—I'm a waiting game world champ at this point. Been playing my whole life, it feels like.

Waited to finally be regarded highly enough to head up the Titans...

Waited to kick...

Which is bad news for this ape.

I remember the night of 'The Great Sherwood Florist Semantics Argument of '97'—a fight so bad we slept in our separate rooms that night.

You maintained that society spends too much of its time cleaning up the messes of people who don't care about anyone but themselves.

I countered that we spend too much of our time cleaning up the messes of MEN who don't care about anyone but themselves.

Sadly, those messes aren't made solely by madmen in costumes on the wrong side of the law, or even low-level pusher trash like punchy here.

They're even made by the men we trust and love.

Grant your servant peace and hear his prayers.

I pray for the center to hold.

I pray for patience.

I pray for humility.

I pray for zen in the face of adversity.

I pray for the delivery of the world outside, from the powers that corrupt it, into the hands of those who seek justice.

I pray that this place gets a television set one day, because I'm really, really bored.

But mostly, I humbly pray for another father, Father.

My own.

Perhaps I shouldn't say that, as I'm not really praying for him, but for me.

I pray for an end to the silliness of my hope that I might one day really know my father as my father.

It's a waste of prayer, I know-- as my father is dead. And how can one ever really know the dead?

I should instead pray for rain. But which kind?

A renewing rain that will fertilize the plantings, and bring forth crops so that I and my brothers might feed those less fortunate than ourselves?

Or a rain that will wash away a child's wish to know and be his father?

It was foolish of me to walk in his shoes, fancying myself a 'hero.'

True heroics are found just as easily in the mundane-- such as harvesting the earth and yielding sustenance from her fertile soil.

One needn't a costume for that.

Though a bow doesn't hurt.

Your servant finds it all so frustrating, Father. I tried so hard to learn who Oliver Queen really was.

I assumed his mantle...

... And even aided his contemporaries.

And despite my best efforts, I knew the man no better than when I started the journey.

So I returned here, hoping to find some part of him in a place I hadn't thought to look before: within myself.

But even in the solitude of this holy place, I still do not know my father any better than I did in the outside world.

So now I pray for an end to it.

As the soil accepts the seed, I pray you grant your servant the ability to accept that he will never know his father.

At least until he, too, is in the ground.

Grant me the patience to wait for that, Father.

Grant me the patience....

STAR CITY, THE ONE-TIME HOME OF GREEN ARROW.

AND STANLEY DOVER'S PATIENCE IS WEARING THIN.

JUST KEEPS GETTING WORSE AND WORSE...

GONNA HAVE TO PULL UP THE STAKES SOON.

YOU HEAR THAT, ALEX? THE OLD MAN DOESN'T LIKE STAR CITY ANYMORE. HE THINKS IT'S TOO ROUGH OR SOMETHING. HE WANTS OUT.

ONLY ONE WAY OUTTA THIS PLACE, GRAMPS...

...AND IT AIN'T THE STAR CITY EXPRESS.

IT'S THE .38 SPECIAL.

HEN IT STARTS, IT ALWAYS STARTS SMALL.

SO SMALL THAT THE ORIGIN ALMOST ALWAYS GOES UNNOTICED.

ALMOST...

THUNK!

AAGGH!

BAF!

ACK!

WHAT'S THE MATTER, CHUM?

OH, MY GOD...

VERY "DICK VAN DYKE."

Heh heh.

HEY, UH... I DON'T THINK THIS IS--

PAF!

DON'T THINK, POOPSIE... JUST PEEL. NOW.

OR ELSE. 'KAY?

OH, MAN...

YOU KNOW, WHEN I WAS IN HIGH SCHOOL, I NEVER SCORED CUTE LITTLE GIRLS LIKE YOU. SEE, I HAD A LOTTA ACNE AND WASN'T REALLY ON WHAT YOU MIGHT CALL THE ATHLETIC SIDE.

BACK THEN, A GIRL LIKE YOU? NEVER WOULD'VE EVEN WASTED THE BREATH ON ME TO CALL ME A NERD.

THANK GOD WE DON'T STAY IN HIGH SCHOOL FOREVER, HUH?

BUT THANK GOD, ALSO, THAT WE CAN RISE TO A POSITION IN LIFE WHERE WE CAN MAKE UP FOR LOST TIME, AND DO ALL THOSE THINGS WE COULDN'T BACK IN OUR MORE AWKWARD AND LESS POWERFUL DAYS.

6

8

UM... THANKS, MISTER.

YOU REALLY WANT TO THANK ME, GO A LOT EASIER ON THE ROUGE.

HEY! UNF!

HERE'S AN OPTION... BE A DOLL AND CLOSE THE DOOR ON YOUR WAY OUT, WOULD YOU?

'BYE, KIDDO.

CLICK!

WHO'S THIS WALKIE-TALKIE REACH, FAT-CAT?

WH-WHAT?!

WHAT'S ITS RANGE? SHOULD I BE EXPECTING ANOTHER ONE OF YOUR GOONS FROM DOWN THE HALL OR SOMETHING?

I... IT'S A C...CEL PHONE. IT... IT CAN REACH ANY... ANYONE!

IT CAN, HUH? WHO DO YOU THINK YOU ARE WITH A GADGET LIKE THAT? THE BATMAN?

STOLEN CITY FUNDS CAN BUY A LOT OF HIGH-TECH TOYS, CAN'T IT?

H-HOW'D YOU...?

I KNOW A LOT OF THINGS ABOUT YOU, PAL.

THE ONLY THING I DON'T KNOW IS WHAT YOU'RE GONNA TELL ME RIGHT NOW.

HOW'D YOU GET THE GIRL, COUNCILMAN? SHE COULDN'T HAVE BEEN MORE THAN FIFTEEN. WORD HAS IT YOU LIKE 'EM YOUNG AND ILLEGAL.
BUT I'M WONDERING IF YOUR DEVIANT APPETITES HAVE GONE BEYOND SIMPLY SEXUALLY FOULING STAR CITY YOUTH, AND CROSSED OVER INTO BLOODLETTING?

Y-YOU TH-THINK I'M THE ST-STAR CITY SLAYER?! I SWEAR TO G-GOD I'M NOT! R-RICHARD... TH-THE P-PIMP! HE SENDS THE GUH-GIRLS OVER! B-BUT I... I N-NEVER KILLED NO K-KIDS!

10

THE ESPLANADE HOTEL, DOWNTOWN STAR CITY.

ONLY A FEW MORE HOURS UNTIL THE ELEVEN O'CLOCK NEWS.

STAR CITY YOUTH RECREATIONAL CENTER
A PLACE FOR OUR CITY'S KIDS

YOU IN THERE, MIA?

YEAH, COME IN.

HEY, KID.

LITTLE TROUBLE UPTOWN TONIGHT?

NOTHING I COULDN'T HANDLE.

HEARD YOU DIDN'T HANDLE IT... SOMEONE ELSE DID.

A COSTUME, HE SHOT THE PLACE UP WITH ARROWS.

CAN'T SAY I'M NOT GLAD ABOUT IT, EITHER.

COME ON OVER AND TELL 'UNCLE' RICHARD ALL ABOUT IT.

THAT GUY-- THE ONE YOU SET ME UP WITH? HE WAS A REAL PERV, RICHARD. I WAS KIND OF AFRAID OF HIM. HE WAS TAKING PICTURES OF ME AND SORT OF ROUGHING ME UP.

DID HE HURT YOU? IF HE DID, I'LL KILL HIM.

NO, HE DIDN'T. BUT IT FELT-- I DON'T KNOW... WEIRD.

LIKE, I CAN'T SAY FOR SURE HE WASN'T GOING TO HURT ME.

HE WAS SOME SORT'A POLITICAL GUY.

12

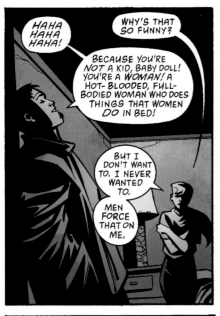

HA HA HA HA HAHA!

WHY'S THAT SO FUNNY?

BECAUSE YOU'RE *NOT A KID*, BABY DOLL! YOU'RE A *WOMAN!* A HOT-BLOODED, FULL-BODIED WOMAN WHO DOES THINGS THAT WOMEN *DO* IN BED!

BUT I DON'T WANT TO. I NEVER WANTED TO.

MEN FORCE THAT ON ME.

SO NOW I *FORCE* MYSELF ON YOU, IS THAT IT?

I DIDN'T MEAN IT LIKE THAT...

NOW I'M NO BETTER THAN YOUR OLD MAN, IS THAT IT?

I'M SORRY, RICHARD. DON'T--

THIS IS THE *THANKS* I GET, RIGHT?! I TREAT YOU LIKE A DAMN QUEEN AND FEED YOU AND CLOTHE YOU AND GIVE YOU A PLACE TO LIVE, AND I'M NO BETTER THAN YOUR RAPIST FATHER, IS THAT IT?!

RICHARD! PLEASE--!

I WAS TRYING TO DO THIS *NICE*, MIA! I WANTED TO CUDDLE YOU BEFORE I HAD TO DO WHAT I GOTTA DO-- BECAUSE I *LOVE* YOU!

WHAT ARE YOU *TALKING* ABOUT, RICHARD?! WHAT DO YOU GOTTA DO...?

I GOTTA MAKE SURE *YOU* DON'T LEAD BACK TO *ME*. YOU SCREWED UP, BABY. WORD ABOUT WHAT WENT DOWN UPTOWN IS ALL OVER THE STREETS! THE COPS *ALREADY* BUSTED DREYFUS, WHICH MEANS THAT THE MASKED-MAN'S ON *THEIR* SIDE! AND IF HE SAW YOU THERE, HOW LONG BEFORE HE TRACES YOU BACK TO ME?

B-BUT HE WASN'T AFTER ME OR YUH-YOU, RICHARD...

I'M SORRY, MAMA MIA, BUT I CAN'T TAKE THAT *CHANCE*. I CAN'T DO NO TIME FOR NO LITTLE *GIRL'S* STUPID MISTAKE.

NO!

NOW THIS...

...THIS COULD LEAD OFF THE ELEVEN O'CLOCK NEWS...

...BUT MIA DEARDEN HAS JUST REALIZED THAT SHE HAS NO DESIRE TO BE ON TV.

OW!

OOF!

HURK!

KSSSH!

CR-CRAZY HUAGH!

YOU DON'T LOVE ME, RICHARD. PEOPLE WHO LOVE PEOPLE DON'T *RAPE* THEM, OR MAKE THEM HAVE SEX WITH STRANGERS FOR MONEY.

OR TRY TO KILL THEM.

C-C'MON, Mm-MAMA Mm-MIA... IWASJUSS FUH-FOOLIN' ROUND...

I'M *FIFTEEN*, RICHARD. I SHOULD BE IN *HIGH SCHOOL*, WONDERING WHAT I'M GOING TO *WEAR* TOMORROW, NOT WORRYING THAT YOU'RE GOING TO *SLIT MY THROAT* FOR MESSING UP YOUR BUSINESS--

-- AND YOUR BUSINESS IS *SELLING MY BODY* TO ANY LOSER WITH FIFTY BUCKS!

WELL, NOT ANY-MORE.

GIVE ME YOUR HAND.

W-WHY DO Y-YUH-YOU WANT MY HUH-HAND?

I'M MAKING A LIFE-CHANGE HERE, AND I WANT TO MAKE SURE YOU KNOW I'M *SERIOUS*.

NOW BITE DOWN *HARD*, THIS IS GOING TO *HURT*.

WH-WHAT?!

AAAHH!

OH, GOD! AAHHH!

I CUT THE TENDON BETWEEN YOUR THUMB AND POINTER FINGER, YOU CAN GET IT FIXED, BUT THE OPERATION'S PAINFUL. IT HAPPENED TO MY MOTHER ONCE, BEFORE SHE DIED. SHE'D CUT HERS FIXING MY FATHER A SANDWICH.

DON'T FOLLOW ME, RICHARD, PLEASE. IF YOU DO, THEN I'LL CUT THE OTHER ONE, AND IF YOU STILL TRY TO FIND ME AFTER THAT, THEN I'LL CUT YOUR THROAT.

I SWEAR TO GOD.

NOT QUITE WORTHY OF THE ELEVEN O'CLOCK NEWS AS IT WOULD HAVE BEEN IF THE TABLES HADN'T BEEN TURNED, TRUE...

15

HE'S A SCUM-LORD OF THE HIGHEST ORDER, BUT HE'S NOT THE STAR CITY SLAYER. REGARDLESS, I LEFT HIM GIFT-WRAPPED FOR THE BLUE FASCISTS TO DEAL WITH.

LIKE FINDS, I GUESS.

THIS INTELLIGENCE CAME IN WHILE YOU WERE OUT. THERE'S RUMOR OF A CHILD SLAVERY RING THAT'S BEING RUN OUT OF STAR CITY.

COULD HAVE SOMETHING TO DO WITH THE SLAYER, NO?

AS GOOD A PLACE TO CHECK AS ANY. THAT'S ON TOMORROW'S MENU.

THANK GOD YOU KNOW HOW TO HANDLE THAT GLORIFIED TOASTER. IT'S BEYOND ME. THEY USED TO HAVE STUFF LIKE THAT ON THE SATELLITE, BUT I STAYED AS FAR AWAY FROM IT AS I COULD.

THERE'S NOTHING WRONG WITH A LITTLE TECHNOLOGY, OLIVER. PROGRESS IS THE WAY OF THE WORLD.

NOT MINE, THANKS. GIVE ME A BOW AND ARROW AND A GOOD RIGHT HOOK, AND I CAN GATHER ALL THE INTELLIGENCE A SCARED SECOND-STORY MAN CAN BLAB BEFORE PASSING OUT AND WETTING HIMSELF.

I TAKE IT YOU USED A LOT OF THE NEW ARSENAL TO EMPTY BLADDERS TONIGHT.

I SEE THE BOLO-ARROW'S ALREADY GONE. THE TIME-BOMB ARROW, TOO.

I DON'T UNDERSTAND HOW SO MANY PEOPLE CAN AFFORD TO BE COSTUMED VIGILANTES. IT'S SO EXPENSIVE. BETWEEN THE OUTFITS, THE HARDWARE, THE GADGETS...

TAKE YOU, FOR EXAMPLE: YOU WORK PRETTY SIMPLE-- JUST THE BOW AND ARROW. BUT THE AMOUNT OF ARROWS YOU MUST LEAVE BEHIND ALL IN A NIGHT'S WORK WOULD BREAK A MAN OF MODERATE MEANS.

I HAVE YOU TO THANK FOR THAT, STANLEY. AND I DO THANK YOU-- FROM THE BOTTOM OF MY HEART. YOU PUTTING ME UP, LAYING OUT THE JACK FOR ALL THE EQUIPMENT AND THE SUITS, LETTING ME OPERATE OUT OF THIS ROOM...

WELL, DON'T EVER THINK A DAY GOES BY THAT I DON'T APPRECIATE YOU HELPING ME GET BACK ON MY FEET.

WHAT'D I TELL YOU? YOU DON'T OWE ME NOTHING. YOU SAVED MY LIFE, OLIVER. AND IN THAT MOMENT, I REALIZED THAT A FORTUNE SITTING IN THE BANK COLLECTING INTEREST COULD BE PUT TO BETTER USE EQUIPPING AND AIDING THE ONLY HERO THIS CITY EVER HAD.

AND AS IF THAT'S NOT ENOUGH, HELPING YOU GIVES AN OLD, RICH MAN'S LIFE SOME NOBLE PURPOSE HE MIGHT'VE DIED WITHOUT KNOWING.

YOU AIN'T GOING *ANY-WHERE*, YOU *FOSSIL,* YOU GOT PLENTY OF GOOD LIFE LEFT IN YOU. BUT YOU'RE NOT MY BUTLER, SO I'D APPRECIATE YOU *NOT* PICKING UP AFTER ME.

I KNOW WHAT YOU'RE *SAYING,* THOUGH, I REMEMBER WHAT IT WAS *LIKE* TO BE A RICH MAN MYSELF. BEFORE I GAVE UP MY *OWN* FORTUNE A FEW YEARS BACK, I HAD TO DEAL WITH THE *GUILT* OF BEING *TO-THE-MANNER-BORN.*

UNTIL I STARTED *THIS* GIG, I FELT LIKE A WASTE OF GOOD AIR LIKE *BRUCE WAYNE,* OR SOMETHING.

SLINGING THESE PUPPIES FOR RIGHT, NOT MIGHT, SURE OPENED MY EYES, SHOWED ME A WHOLE DIFFERENT AMERICA THAN I'D EVER REALIZED WAS OUT THERE.

I JUST WISH I COULD REMEMBER *WHY* I WAS LIKE I WAS WHEN WE FOUND EACH OTHER IN THAT ALLEY, AND WHAT HAPPENED TO MY *APARTMENT.*

HELL-- I JUST WISH I COULD REMEMBER *WHAT HAPPENED* TO ME!

NOW, NOW-- LET'S NOT START *THIS* AGAIN. YOU KNOW YOU GET THOSE *MIGRAINES* FROM THINKING ABOUT IT TOO MUCH. WE'LL GET TO THE *BOTTOM* OF IT EVENTUALLY.

WHO KNOWS-- MAYBE IT EVEN HAS SOMETHING TO DO WITH THE *STAR SLAYER,* BUT RIGHT NOW, *THAT* SHOULD BE OUR *ONLY* GOAL... FINDING THE SLAYER AND BRINGING HIM, OR HER, TO JUSTICE.

"HER"?!

C'MON, STANLEY-- YOU'RE SUPPOSED TO BE EVEN *LESS* ENLIGHTENED THAN ME, BEING AN OLD MAN FROM ANOTHER GENERATION AND ALL, BUT AS *LIBERAL* AS *I* AM, I WON'T GO SO FAR OUT ON A LIMB AS TO SUPPOSE FOR A MINUTE THAT A *WOMAN* COULD BE CAPABLE OF A CRIME AS *UGLY* AS THE SLAYER'S.

A WOMAN WANTS TO WORK THE WRONG SIDE OF THE LAW, SHE THROWS ON A *CAT SUIT...* SHE DOESN'T KIDNAP KIDS AND *GUT* THEM.

SPEAKING OF WHICH, HOW WOULD YOU LIKE TO CHOKE DOWN SOME FILET MIGNON I JUST GRILLED? IT'S MARINATED IN BALSAMIC AND BASIL.

LEAD THE WAY, SENIOR CITIZEN. I'M AS HUNGRY AS IT GETS.

I JUST GOT ONE QUESTION FOR YOU, THOUGH.

WHAT'S THAT?

DO YOU DO DISHES, TOO? BECAUSE IF YOU DO, I'VE GOT NO CHOICE BUT TO JUST *MARRY* YOU.

YOU'RE TOO OLD FOR ME, JUNIOR. I MEAN, TOO *YOUNG* FOR ME.

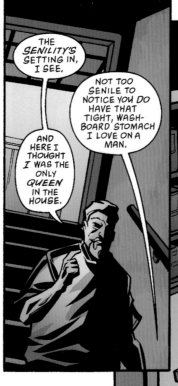

THE *SENILITY'S* SETTING IN, I SEE.

NOT TOO *SENILE* TO NOTICE YOU *DO* HAVE THAT TIGHT, WASH-BOARD STOMACH I LOVE ON A MAN.

AND HERE I THOUGHT I WAS THE ONLY *QUEEN* IN THE HOUSE.

TWO GRILLED-TO-PERFECTION FILET MIGNONS LATER...

ANY OF YOUR FRIENDS TRY TO CONTACT YOU YET? THE FELLA WITH THE MAGIC RING, OR THE BLONDE LADY IN FISHNETS-- THE ONE I USED TO SEE PICTURES OF YOU WITH IN THE PAPERS?

NO, THANK GOD. LANTERN'S A PAL, BUT HE'S A LITTLE TOO *DRIVEN* IN MY BOOK. IT'S GOOD TO GET A *BREAK* AWAY FROM HIM NOW AND THEN. I MEAN, WE JUST SPENT ALL THAT TIME TOGETHER ON THE ROAD, NOT TOO LONG AGO. THAT'LL COVER ME FOR AWHILE.

I'M SURE THE LITTLE *BLUE GUYS* HAVE GOT HIM CHASING DOWN PURPLE PEOPLE-EATERS UP IN THE STARS, ANYWAY.

FINISHED?

THANKS.

THE *LADY-BIRD* I MISS, THOUGH. FEELS LIKE A *DOG'S AGE* SINCE I SEEN *HER.* DON'T GET ME *WRONG*-- I DIG YOUR COMPANY, WRINKLES. BUT YOU DON'T SMELL NEARLY AS PRETTY AS *HER,* AND YOU MAKE A *HELLUVA* STEAK, AS GOOD AS *HERS,* EVEN-- BUT I'M NONE TOO *CURIOUS* TO FIND OUT IF YOU CAN MATCH HER *OTHER* DOMESTIC SKILLS, IF YOU CATCH MY DRIFT.

YOU'RE SUCH A TEASE.

ARE YOU WORRIED ABOUT NOT HEARING FROM HER?

NAH-- SHE'S A LIBERATED WOMAN WHO CAN MORE THAN TAKE CARE OF HER-SELF. SHE'S HER MOTHER'S DAUGHTER, THAT'S FOR SURE.

AND WHEN SHE WORKS, SHE GOES UNDERGROUND. *DEEP* UNDERGROUND. SOMETIMES, I DON'T HEAR FROM HER FOR WEEKS.

DO YOU EVER *WORRY* ABOUT HER? I MEAN, YOU'RE BOTH IN A ROUGH JOB-- *ESPECIALLY* FOR A WOMAN, I'D IMAGINE.

PLEASE-- SHE SHOULD WORRY ABOUT *ME.* I'M JUST SOME *SCHMO* WHAT LIKES TO SHOOT ARROWS AT *BAD GUYS.* SHE'S A *SUPER HERO* OF THE HIGHEST ORDER, WITH *POWERS* AND WHATNOT. SHE'S GOT THIS *SONIC SCREAM* THAT CAN BLOW YOUR EARDRUMS OUT.

I HELP HER WHEN SHE ASKS, BUT SHE CAN CERTAINLY HANDLE *HERSELF.*

19

I TELL YOU WHO I *DON'T* MISS, IS THE *REST* OF THE DAMN *LEAGUERS*, BIG RED AND THE LONG-EARED *GHOUL*-- THOSE TWO GIVE ME THE *CREEPS*, THE FISH GUY ISN'T ALL THAT BAD, THOUGH..., AND THE *MARTIAN'S* A GOOD EGG, A LITTLE TOO *SERIOUS* ALL THE TIME, BUT STILL A GOOD EGG, HE CAN *SHAPE-SHIFT*, TOO. FOUND *THAT* OUT BACK WHEN WE...

AM I *BORING* YOU?

I JUST DIDN'T KNOW I WAS LIVING WITH A *TV STAR.*

WOW, *THAT* DIDN'T TAKE LONG.

TURN IT *UP*.

..., TOWN PENTHOUSE APARTMENT OF COUNCILMAN *FREDDY DREYFUS*-- THE DISTRICT'S LEADING VOICE IN THE CITY'S WAR ON DRUGS, BUT IT WAS DRUGS THAT MAY BE BEHIND TONIGHT'S RAID-- A RAID THAT *WASN'T* TRIGGERED BY POLICE,

THERE WAS EVIDENCE OF MANY STRUGGLES, THE USE OF INCENDIARY *DEVICES,* AND ABOUT TEN TO TWENTY DIFFERENT PROJECTILES, AS YOU CAN SEE,

ARROWS,

YES, THE KIND WE HAVEN'T SEEN AROUND THESE PARTS IN YEARS,

WHICH BEGS THE QUESTION, JUST *WHO* COULD THIS MYSTERIOUS VIGILANTE BE? COULD STAR CITY'S OWN *EMERALD ARCHER* BE BACK IN ACTION? THE CRIMINAL ELEMENT IN TOWN WOULD DO WELL TO START *PRAYING* THAT HE'S NOT.

"BACK IN ACTION"?! WHAT DO THEY *MEAN?* I NEVER *LEFT.*

REPORTING LIVE FROM UPTOWN STAR CITY, I'M TOVAH HERNANDEZ CARLSON,

20

NINETY-NINE...?!

WHY DON'T YOU PUT THE ARROW AWAY NOW, BEFORE SOMEONE GETS HURT, OLD-TIMER?

THATTABOY, POPS...

NOW, HOW ABOUT A SHOT OF BOURBON TO CALM THOSE NERVES WHILE WE WAIT FOR THE POL--

Uhn...!

SWAK!

'Old-timer? Smart-ass kid. But not smart enough to lock his file cabinet.

Gotta be something in here that'll clean up what the hell's going on.

Something incriminating...

WHAT THE...?!

recommendations for th
city budget increase,
to the uncontrollable
of refugees from the
remains of Coast City
Since federal
not forthcomin
be allocated

ARE YOU ALL RIGHT IN THERE?

NO...

NO, I'M NOT...

MISTER LEEDS?

6

LET'S SEE IF YOU CAN GET *THIS ONE* PAST ME...

THE STAR CITY YOUTH CENTER, LATER THAT DAY...

INCOMING!

NICE ONE!

YOU IN CHARGE HERE?

YOU GOT IT, JIMMY! YOU GOT IT!

POOM!

IF YOU CAN CALL IT TH--

HEY!

I MEAN...

HELLO, *YOUNG LADY.* WHAT CAN I DO FOR YOU?

I DON'T KNOW. WHAT *CAN* YOU DO FOR ME?

I GOT THE IMPRESSION I WAS SUPPOSED TO *COME* HERE FROM THIS *CARD.*

OH, YEAH-- THE GREEN ARROW *TOLD* ME A PRETTY, YOUNG GIRL *MIGHT* BE STOPPING BY...

HE ASKED IF I COULD GIVE HER A *JOB* WORKING WITH THE KIDS?

YO, OLLIE! YOU IN OR OUT?

CLOSED

WHY DON'T *YOU* PITCH FOR AWHILE, JUAN? I'VE GOT TO TALK TO THE *LADY* HERE FOR A MINUTE.

AND REMEMBER-- IT'S *KICKBALL,* NOT *DODGE-BALL.*

7

SO, HOW ABOUT IT? YOU GOOD WITH KIDS?

GREEN ARROW SAID HE THOUGHT YOU MIGHT BE ABLE TO THROW A HELLUVA KICKBALL.

WHAT'S ALL THIS "GREEN ARROW SAID" GARBAGE?

WE'RE CLOSE-- ME AND GREEN ARROW.

WHAT AM I, STUPID OR SOMETHING?

YOU ARE THE GREEN ARROW!

HOW DID...? WHEN DID...? WHO TOLD YOU?

Oh, PLEASE! I'M NOT A TOTAL IDIOT! THAT LITTLE MASK YOU WEAR DOESN'T EXACTLY BATMAN YOUR FACE.

AND THE BEARD'S A DEAD GIVE-AWAY, TOO.

YOU WANNA BLOW MY SECRET IDENTITY?! KEEP YOUR VOICE DOWN.

YOU KEEP YOUR VOICE DOWN-- OR AT LEAST GO FOR SOMETHING THROATIER WHEN YOU'RE ALL SPROUTED-OUT. YOU TALK IN THE SAME VOICE OUT-OF-COSTUME AS YOU DO WHEN YOU'RE WILLIAM-TELLING IT.

SPROUTED-OUT?

Y'KNOW-- SPROUT? THE JOLLY GREEN GIANT'S LITTLE FRIEND.

SO, HERE'S WHERE YOU TELL ME WHAT KIND OF PAY I CAN EXPECT TO PULL DOWN IN THIS JOINT.

I USED TO WORK AT THE REC CENTER BACK HOME, BEFORE I CAME TO THE CITY.

WHATEVER IT IS, I'M SURE IT'S NOT GONNA BE WHAT I WAS MAKING WITH RICHARD.

RICHARD?

THE KILLER PIMP. THE ONE THAT AIN'T SUCH A KILLER AFTER LAST NIGHT.

I GOT YOU TO THANK FOR THAT.

ME? YOU MEAN GREEN ARROW.

GIVE IT UP ALREADY, JEEZ.

OH, AND I'M GONNA NEED A PLACE TO CRASH.

YO, KID! THE MAN SAID NO DODGEBALL! YOU BEAN ONE MORE KICKER AND I'M PANTSING YOU!

8

HOLD ON THERE, SPEEDY! YOU'RE MOVING QUICKER THAN THAT GUY IN THE *RED SUIT!*

I THINK *FAST,* I TALK *FAST.* TRY TO KEEP UP, OLD-TIMER.

AGAIN WITH THE 'OLD-TIMER.'

YOU'RE *RIGHT*-- THE PAY'S *TERRIBLE.* BUT THE BOSS IS A *SWEETHEART.* AND IF YOU NEED A PLACE TO STAY, I THINK I CAN COVER YOU...

... *TEMPORARILY.*

SOUNDS *DELISH.*

PROVIDING...

PROVIDING *WHAT?*

PROVIDING OUR LITTLE 'SPROUT' SECRET STAYS *BETWEEN US.*

CAPISCE?

SURE-- US AND ANYONE WITH *HALF A BRAIN* AND *ONE EYE* OPEN.

I'M MIA, MIA DEARDEN.

OLIVER QUEEN.

WELL, OLIVER QUEEN-- YOU GOT YOURSELF A NEW *PARTNER.*

PARTNER?

NOW DO ME A *SOLID* AND STOW THIS SOMEWHERE SAFE. I GOTTA TEACH THESE *LATCH-KEYS* HOW TO PLAY SOME *SERIOUS* KICKBALL-- NOT THIS OLD MAN'S *NONSENSE* YOU'RE SELLING 'EM.

LISTEN UP, YOU LITTLE *PUKES!* WE PLAY TO *ELEVEN!* GROUND-OUTS AND POP-OUTS ARE *LEGIT,* BUT YOU GOTTA *TAG* THE RUNNER-- NOT *STONE* HIM! I CATCH YOU *THUNDERBALLING* IT, AND YOU SIT OUT AT *LEAST A PERIOD!*

UH...

WELCOME ABOARD?

AND IF YOU KICK IT *OVER THE FENCE* YOU GOTTA FETCH IT YOURSELF! SO EASY ON THE *POWER-FOOTS!*

FRIEND OF YOURS?

SHE IS *NOW,* KID'S WHAT YOU MIGHT CALL A *WHIRLING DERVISH.* SHE'S AS SUBTLE AS AN 'A' BOMB.

YOU'RE GONNA HAVE TO ADD ANOTHER *CHECK* TO THE *PAYROLL.*

ABOUT *TIME* YOU HIRED SOME *HELP.*

YOU'LL HAVE TO *INTRODUCE US* WHEN THE GAME'S UP.

STAR CITY YOUTH CENTER

YOU'VE GOT *ALL NIGHT* TO MEET AND GREET WITH HER. SHE'S THE NEW *OLLIE QUEEN,* AS FAR AS DOVER HOUSE *BOARDERS* GO.

SHE'S *MOVING IN WITH US?*

I'LL EXPLAIN *LATER.* MEANTIME, CAN YOU DRIVE HER *HOME* WHEN WE CLOSE?

BEFORE I FOLLOW UP ON THAT LEAD FROM LAST NIGHT, I'VE GOT SOMETHING *PERSONAL* I WANT TO LOOK INTO.

THE STAR CITY BUS TERMINAL...

NEXT!

SIR...?

GOTHAM
ETROPO
EW YOR
S A
EONARD
CHICAG
UR CIT

SIR! YOU'RE HOLDING UP THE LINE!

GOTHAM
METROPOLIS
NEW YORK
ANGELES
NARDO

CHICAG
HUB C
KEYST
CENTRA
RED B

OH-- I'M SORRY. GOT A LITTLE LOST THERE.

WHAT CITY, SIR?

Uh, ROUND TRIP TO COAST CITY, PLEASE.

YOU'RE KIDDING, RIGHT?

NO, I WANT A TICKET TO THE COAST CITY BUS STATION, AND THEN ANOTHER TICKET THAT'LL GET ME BACK HERE.

WHERE I'M FROM, THAT'S CALLED A ROUND-TRIP.

WHERE I'M FROM, THAT'S CALLED A HEAD-TRIP.

LOOK, LADY-- JUST GIVE ME THE TICKETS.

OH, RIGHT AWAY, SIR, BUT I GOTTA WARN YOU, THE COAST CITY ROUTE GOES BY WAY OF ATLANTIS AND NARNIA. IS THAT GOING TO BE A PROBLEM FOR YOU?

WHAT THE HELL ARE YOU--?

WE'RE A LITTLE BUSY FOR GAMES TODAY, JOKER JUNIOR! NOW BEAT IT BEFORE I CALL A COP!

NEXT!

10

I GUESS HE *DOES,* BUT HIS HOME BASE SEEMS TO BE *METROPOLIS.*

SO, OLLIE'S THE SUPERMAN OF STAR CITY?

HE *WAS,* BUT HE MOVED TO SEATTLE YEARS AGO.

AND NOW HE'S *COME BACK?*

WELL, THAT'S THE *STRANGE* PART...

..., SEE, THE MAN IS *SUPPOSED* TO BE *DEAD.*

DEAD?

YUP. WORD WAS HE *DIED* IN A PLANE ACCIDENT. A *BOMB* OR SOMETHING *BLEW* A JET UP, AND HE WAS *KILLED* TRYING TO *DISARM* IT.

I'VE EVEN SEEN A *PICTURE* OF HIS *GRAVE* IN ONE OF THE GOSSIP RAGS.

YEAH, BUT DON'T THESE GUYS 'DIE' ALL THE *TIME?* LIKE, DIDN'T *SUPERMAN* DIE ONCE? AND THEN THERE WERE, LIKE, A *BUNCH* OF GUYS WHO WERE TRYING TO TAKE OVER FOR HIM UNTIL HE SUDDENLY *CAME BACK?*

THE *DIFFERENCE,* I THINK, IS THAT *SUPERMAN* IS AN *ALIEN* AND *OLLIE* IS JUST A *HUMAN BEING.*

SUPERMAN'S AN *ALIEN? NO WAY!*

SURE, AND WHO KNOWS HOW HIS BODY WORKS COMPARED TO *OURS* -- ASIDE FROM THE *OBVIOUS* DIFFERENCES.

BUT *UNLIKE* SUPERMAN, IF OLLIE *DIED* IN THAT PLANE CRASH, HE SHOULD HAVE *STAYED DEAD.* YET HE WALKS, TALKS, EATS, AND SLEEPS -- ALL BEHAVIOR *NORMALLY* ASSOCIATED WITH THE *LIVING.*

YEAH-- DRESSING UP AND SHOOTING *ARROWS* AT MUGGERS AND PIMPS IS *NORMAL,* ALL RIGHT.

WHICH WAS *ANOTHER* THING I WANTED TO ASK-- WASN'T THERE A *DIFFERENT* GREEN ARROW FOR AWHILE? A *KID,* LIKE? HE WAS IN THE *JUSTICE LEAGUE?*

THERE *WAS,* BUT I'VE NEVER *BROUGHT IT UP.* I DON'T THINK OLLIE *KNOWS* ABOUT HIM. IN FACT, HE DOESN'T KNOW MUCH *ABOUT ANYTHING* THAT'S HAPPENED OVER THE LAST *DECADE* OR SO.

IT'S LIKE YOU WERE SAYING BEFORE-- HE'S KIND OF *STOPPED IN TIME.* THE NEAREST I CAN FIGURE IS HE'S SUFFERING FROM SOME SORT OF *AMNESIA.*

THAT STUFF'S *REAL?* I THOUGHT THEY MADE THAT UP FOR *SOAP OPERAS* AND *MOVIES!*

AMNESIA'S *RARE,* BUT IN THIS CASE, PRETTY *REAL.*

FROM WHAT I'VE READ ON THE SUBJECT, *AMNESIACS* HAVE TO BE BROUGHT UP TO SPEED *VERY SLOWLY.* YOU CAN'T *SHOCK* THEM WITH TOO MUCH NEW INFORMATION ALL AT ONCE.

THAT'S WHY EVERYTHING SEEMS KIND OF *DATED* IN THIS HOUSE.

I WAS *WONDERING* WHY A GUY *LOADED* ENOUGH TO HAVE A SWANK *BROWNSTONE* ON PARK DIDN'T OWN A MICROWAVE, OR A *DVD* PLAYER, OR EVEN HAVE *CABLE.*

IT WASN'T *ALWAYS* THAT WAY AROUND HERE. I USED TO BE A *HIGH-TECH NUT.* I HAD ALL THE LATEST *GADGETS.*

SO, WHAT HAPPENED?

I MET OLLIE... WELL, REALLY I MET GREEN ARROW, FIRST.

MUST'VE BEEN SHOCKING MEETING A GUY YOU THOUGHT WAS DEAD.

I DON'T KNOW WHAT SHOCKED ME MORE THAT NIGHT: ALMOST GETTING GUNNED DOWN BY A PACK OF BACK-ALLEY PSYCHOPATHS...

"I MEAN, HERE WAS A LEGEND-- LOOKING MORE DISHEVELED AND DISORIENTED THAN PEOPLE I'VE GIVEN SPARE CHANGE TO OUTSIDE OF SUPER-MARKETS-- COLLAPSING RIGHT IN FRONT OF ME!

"... OR LAYING EYES ON THE ONCE-GREAT EMERALD ARCHER, NOW REDUCED TO TATTERED RAGS AND A MAKESHIFT, TRASH-CRAFTED ARSENAL.

"I DIDN'T WANT TO CALL IN THE POLICE. I MEAN, THIS MAN HAD BEEN THE CITY'S HERO FOR YEARS. WHAT WOULD THE PRESS DO TO HIM ONCE WORD GOT OUT THAT GREEN ARROW WASN'T DEAD--

"-- THAT INSTEAD HE WAS A HOMELESS VAGRANT WHO'D MAYBE LOST HIS MARBLES?

SO I BROUGHT HIM BACK HERE.

"IT WAS A LONG FEW WEEKS. HE'D COME AND GO, IN AND OUT OF CONSCIOUSNESS, BABBLING WILDLY, MAKING NO SENSE.

"WHEN HE WAS COHERENT, HE SEEMED CONFUSED AND SOMETIMES EVEN FRIGHTENED BY HIS SURROUNDINGS.

"ONCE OR TWICE, HE EVEN THOUGHT I WAS A SUPER-VILLAIN-- BASED SOLELY ON THE FACT THAT I HAD A NEW COMPUTER.

"I FIGURED RATHER THAN RISK DISTURBING HIM FURTHER, I'D CLEAR THE HOUSE OF ALL THE DOOHICKEYS AND HARDWARE THAT MIGHT UPSET HIM, AND RE-OUTFIT THE JOINT WITH OLDER STUFF."

YOU SURE DID A GOOD JOB. IT FEELS LIKE THE EIGHTIES NEVER ENDED IN THIS MUSEUM.

THE STUFF YOU'VE SEEN ALREADY ISN'T EVEN THE HALF OF IT. LET ME SHOW YOU THE COMPUTER SET UP WE USE IN THE 'ARROW CAVE.'

'ARROW CAVE'?

OLLIE CALLS IT THAT. I HAVE NO IDEA WHY.

THIS STUFF IS DAMN NEAR *FIFTEEN YEARS OLD*, YOU SHOULD SEE THE BOXES THEY CAME IN-- THEY'RE LABELED PROUDLY *"10K RAM!"*

WHERE'D YOU FIND SOFTWARE THAT *DECREPIT?*

THRIFT SHOPS.

BELIEVE ME-- I *CORNERED* THE MARKET ON OBSOLETE COMPUTER EQUIPMENT, ALONG WITH *PRINCESS PHONES* AND *TOASTER OVENS.*

BUT, IF HE'S OUT THERE IN THE *REAL WORLD* EVERY DAY AND NIGHT-- NOT JUST HERE IN THE *WAYBACK MACHINE*-- DOESN'T HE SEE *MODERN STUFF* ALL OVER THE PLACE?

PLEASE-- ONE *ARCHER* IS ALL THIS HOUSE *NEEDS*, YOUNG LADY.

HONESTLY, I DON'T KNOW *HOW* HE'S COPING WITH THE *OUTSIDE WORLD* SINCE HE INSISTED ON GETTING BACK OUT THERE AND *"FIGHTING THE FAT-CATS,"* AS HE CALLS IT. WHENEVER THE SUBJECT OF HIS *LOST TIME* COMES UP, HE TRIES TO AVOID IT.

YEAH, BUT HE CAN'T AVOID IT *FOREVER.* SOONER OR LATER...

*"... HE'S GONNA HAVE TO *DEAL WITH IT.*"*

What the hell's *happening* to me?

It's like Coast City's been *wiped off the map*, and nobody seems *shocked* by that.

Or is it, what the hell *happened* to me?

Durgin's suddenly *gone*, and Mayor Major's *dead?*

I *couldn't* have been away *that* long...

...could I?

Damn you, Jordan...

We just *had* to go to Oa...

WHERE'S THIS MUCH *FUN-DUST* *HEADED* FOR, LADS? I DON'T SEE ANY *BOAT* IN THE HARBOR. WHO'S SUPPOSED TO *PICK IT UP?*

BOOM!

Uhhhhnnn...

WHO THE *HELL--*?

Uh-oh...

Like the man said...

ER 22

19

THE STAR CITY BROWNSTONE OF STANLEY DOVER-- THE GREEN ARROW'S NEW BENEFACTOR...

I'M HARD-CORE!

QUIT HOGGIN' THE CORN, STANLEY!

SORRY. NOW, EXPLAIN THE *DRAW* OF THIS SHOW AGAIN?

THEY'RE CHICK *SUPER-HEROES!* HOW *COOL* IS THAT?! THREE LITTLE GIRLS WHO *KICK BUTT!* AFTER YEARS OF CARTOONS FOR *BOYS,* THERE'S FINALLY SOMETHING WORTH WATCHING THAT *GIRLS* CAN EMULATE, TOO.

WHAT ABOUT 'RASPBERRY SHORTCAKES' AND 'RAINBOW SPRITES'? WEREN'T *THOSE* CARTOONS FOR GIRLS, TOO?

THOSE WERE CARTOONS *I* GREW UP WITH, AND LOOK HOW I TURNED OUT.

IT'S ABOUT *TIME* THEY MADE SOMETHING THAT TELLS LITTLE GIRLS THEY DON'T JUST HAVE TO BE *CUTE* OR NICEY-NICE *DOMESTIC.* THEY CAN MAKE JUST AS MUCH *DIFFERENCE* AS ANY STUPID BOY.

AND *SPEAKING* OF STUPID BOYS...

WE INTERRUPT THIS BROADCAST TO BRING YOU A SPECIAL NEWS BULLETIN!

NO! NO!! GET OFF THE SCREEN, YOU LLOYD! GIMME BACK MY 'POWERPOOFS'!

MIA! SHHH!

EXPLOSIVE DEVELOPMENTS IN THE STAR CITY WHARF DISTRICT. LIVE ON THE SCENE IS TOVAH HERNANDEZ CARLSON.

IT LOOKS MORE FITTED ≥Skrtch-tch≥ HOLLYWOOD SOUND-STAGE THAN TO ≥Sktch≥ DISTRICT, BOB. THE MARINE TERRORIST ≥tch≥ ≥Sktch≥ ACK MANTA ≥Skrrtch≥ FIGHT WITH NONE OTHER THAN AQUA-MAN, AND ANOTHER ≥Sktch≥ WHO LOOKS A LOT LIKE STAR CITY'S OLD ≥Skrtch≥

DAMMIT! STUPID ANTIQUE!

THIS IS WHY YOU GOTTA GET CABLE, STANLEY!

I DON'T THINK WE NEED *FIBER-OPTIC* RECEPTION TO FIGURE OUT JUST *WHO* THE WOMAN'S TALKING ABOUT, DO WE?

LOOK'S LIKE OLLIE SKIPPED OUT ON YOUR *PANCAKES...*

IDIOT WEAKLING!

OOF!

CRASH!

uhn!

AHHH!

YOU ALL RIGHT?

I'M FINE! JUST END THIS, FAST!

GREEN ARROW?! WHERE HAVE YOU BEEN?!

IS IT TRUE YOU WERE DEAD?

WHERE'S THE KID-- THE ONE WHO REPLACED YOU?

ARE YOU MAKING STAR CITY YOUR BASE OF OPERATIONS AGAIN?

ARE YOU JACKALS CRAZY OR SOMETHING?!

GET BACK BEHIND THE BARRICADES BEFORE YOU GET YOURSELVES KILLED! WE'RE DEALING WITH A NUT CASE IN A WET SUIT OVER HERE!

"SURE SOUNDS LIKE HIM," THE SEA KING THINKS...

...GIVING HIS ARCH-NEMESIS JUST ENOUGH TIME TO GATHER HIS THOUGHTS...

4

ALL OF WHICH REVOLVE AROUND REGICIDE.

HOW ABOUT THAT, *CURRY?* I CAME HERE TO SMUGGLE CONTRABAND INTO *ATLANTIS*, AND I LEAVE HERE *ICING YOU* IN THE BARGAIN.

ANY IMMORTAL *LAST WORDS* BEFORE I DO YOU LIKE I DID *YOUR KID?*

THWACK...

WHAT?

THWACK

I'd say it stopped three centimeters from his eyeball.

But something tells me...

...that's not where *these two* intend to stop.

5

STILL AS UGLY AS YOUR *SOUL* UNDER THIS OLD GEAR, HUNH?!

WELL, NO MATTER *WHAT* YOU COVER YOURSELF UP WITH, YOU CAN'T HIDE WHAT YOU ARE TO ME-- A SICK *CHILD-KILLER!*

CURRY... NO! PLEASE!

NO MERCY-- *NOT THIS TIME!* THIS TIME...

... YOU'RE NOT GETTING OFF THE HOOK!

AAHHHH!

FFTINGG!

SHWA *SHWA*

What the hell *happened,* Arthur?

What the hell did you *become?*

LATER...

SO HE'S *NOT* DEALING IN THE SLAVE-TRADING OF KIDS?

NO. SOLELY *DRUGS* THIS TIME.

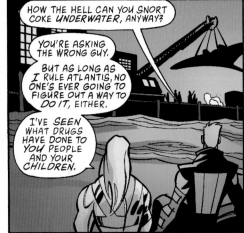

HOW THE HELL CAN YOU SNORT COKE *UNDERWATER,* ANYWAY?

YOU'RE ASKING THE WRONG GUY.

BUT AS LONG AS I RULE ATLANTIS, NO ONE'S EVER GOING TO FIGURE OUT A WAY TO *DO* IT, EITHER.

I'VE SEEN WHAT DRUGS HAVE DONE TO *YOU* PEOPLE AND YOUR *CHILDREN.*

6

BUT THE *PLANE*...! WITH THE *BOMB*...! AND *SUPERMAN* SAID...! AND YOUR *GRAVE* IS...! AND *CONNOR* BECAME...! AND THE *LEAGUE*...!

WOULD YOU QUIT YOUR *BABBLING*, YOU FIVE-FATHOM *FASCIST*!

WHICH *REMINDS* ME-- WHEN THE HELL ARE YOU GOING TO ALLOW FOR SOME *DEMOCRATIC ELECTIONS* DOWN THERE?! *KINGS* WENT OUT OF STYLE WITH *RELIGIOUS PERSECUTION* IN THIS COUNTRY-- A COUNTRY YOU'RE A DE FACTO *PART OF*, BECAUSE WATER SURROUNDS MOST OF OUR BORDERS!

YOU WANNA HANG WITH THE *LEAGUE*, YOU START ACTIN' LIKE AN *AMERICAN*, AND QUIT HIDIN' BEHIND THAT '*CULTURAL DIFFERENCES*' GARBAGE ABOUT WHY *YOU'RE* ALLOWED TO RUN SOME FARCICAL, AQUATIC *DICTATORSHIP* RIGHT UNDER OUR NOSES, WHEN WE'RE OFF FIGHTING *PSYCHOS* IN FOREIGN COUNTRIES FOR DOING THE SAME THING *YOU* ARE!

YOU GOT ANYTHING YOU WANNA *SPUTTER OUT* NOW, I'M *ALL EARS.*

WELL...?!

OH, OLLIE-- I'VE *MISSED* YOU!

EASY, *FLIPPER.* YOU'RE *MARRIED,* AND I LIKE THE LADIES.

IF YOU'VE GOT A FEW MINUTES, THERE'RE SOME *PEOPLE* WHO I'M SURE WOULD *LOVE* TO SEE YOU.

WHAT THE HECK-- *SURE.* TONIGHT'S BIG LEAD DIDN'T TURN UP MUCH, 'CEPT *VADER-OF-THE-SEA,* SO I GOT SOME *TIME* TO KILL.

BESIDES-- I'M STARTING TO GET *WHALE-WARTS* FROM SITTING ON *SHAMU* HERE.

TWO TO THE *WATCHTOWER,* PLEASE.

HEY, WHO'RE YOU TALKING T--

--OOOOOO!

SO MUCH FOR THAT END OF STAR CITY.

LET'S SEE WHAT'S HAPPENING ELSEWHERE AROUND TOWN...

9

MIA DEARDEN SLEEPS RESTLESSLY.

SHE DREAMS FIRST OF A LIFE OF FEAR AND SHAME-- A LIFE OF BETRAYAL AT THE HANDS OF THOSE SHE LOVED AND TRUSTED MOST.

IT IS A LIFE SHE ABANDONED LONG AGO, BUT IT STILL VISITS HER IN NIGHTMARES FROM TIME TO TIME.

SHE THEN SETTLES INTO DREAMS OF LITTLE GIRLS WHO KICK BUTT, AND ALL IS SUDDENLY WELL.

WHICH IS MORE THAN CAN BE SAID FOR STANLEY.

STANLEY'S HAD TROUBLE SLEEPING FOR SOME TIME NOW, AND AS A RESULT CAN'T REMEMBER HIS DREAMS ANYMORE.

BUT STANLEY'S NOT DWELLING ON THAT RIGHT NOW. NO-- ALL OF THE RECENT ACTIVITY THAT'S GRACED HIS ONCE RELATIVELY QUIET HOME HAS SERVED AS A HELP-FUL DISTRACTION FROM HIS MANY PROBLEMS.

A DISTRACTION, AS WELL AS A SOLUTION.

BUT LET'S NOT PRY TOO DEEPLY INTO STANLEY'S AFFAIRS JUST YET. THERE ARE OTHER SOULS TO BE LOOKED IN ON, HERE IN THE POST-MIDNIGHT QUIET OF STAR CITY...

WHAT'S ALL THE SECRECY ABOUT, ANYWAY?

AND HOW COME *I'M* NOT INVITED?

YOU'RE ON MONITOR DUTY, JUNIOR. BESIDES...

"...THIS IS OLD LEAGUE BUSINESS."

KYLE, ANY WORD BACK YET?

I THINK WALLY JUST BEAMED ABOARD, AQUAMAN. AND J'ONN'S NOT TOO FAR BEHIND. WONDER WOMAN'S BEEN WAITING IN THE CONFERENCE ROOM FOR TWENTY MINUTES.

AND YOU KNOW HOW PATIENT SHE CAN BE...

DID I DREAM THAT MESSAGE FROM AQUAMAN, OR DID HE REALLY CALL US UP HERE FOR A MEETING AT TWO IN THE MORNING?

THIS HAD BETTER BE 'CRISIS-HUGE,' THAT'S ALL I CAN SAY.

IT'S MORE LIKE A NIGHTMARE, I'VE BEEN SITTING AROUND THIS CONFERENCE ROOM FOR TWENTY MINUTES WITHOUT ANY EXPLANATION.

YOU THINK YOU'VE GOT IT BAD? TRY BEING MARRIED AND GETTING A TWO A.M. PHONE CALL.

I SPENT AT LEAST TEN MINUTES ASSURING LINDA I WASN'T HAVING AN AFFAIR!

HE'D BETTER START EXPLAINING HIMSELF SOON. I SWEAR BY THE GODS, I'M ON THE VERGE OF CUTTING HIS OTHER HAND OFF.

I'M IN AGREEMENT WITH DIANA-- THOUGH IT'S NOT ARTHUR'S OTHER HAND I'M THINKING OF DISPOSING WITH.

UH, J'ONN?

YES, WALLACE?

YOUR HEAD'S DOING THAT THING AGAIN.

OH.

THERE.

PERFECT.

WELL, NOT REALLY, BUT YOU KNOW WHAT I MEAN.

ONLY TOO WELL, WALLACE.

14

YOU... uh... YOU NEVER, uh... I NEVER KNEW YOU *CARED*, PRINCESS.

I'M JUST HAPPY TO *SEE YOU*, OLLIE. IT'S *BEEN...*

TOO LONG. *FAR* TOO LONG.

YOU AIN'T GONNA TRY TO *KISS ME, TOO*, ARE YOU, MARVIN?

NO OFFENSE, J'ONN, BUT I DON'T WANT YOU *SWIMMING AROUND* IN MY HEAD.

UNDERSTOOD. I MERELY FELT THERE WERE SOME *QUESTIONS* WE ALL HAD THAT COULD BE ANSWERED QUICKLY BY AN *OVERVIEW* OF YOUR THOUGHTS AND MEMORIES.

NO, BUT WITH YOUR *PERMISSION*, OLIVER, I'D LIKE TO TAKE A QUICK SCAN OF YOUR *MIND*.

AFTER THE BIG LADY'S *GREETING*, IT DOESN'T TAKE A *TELEPATH* TO FIGURE OUT WHAT'S ON *MY* MIND, IF YOU CATCH MY *DRIFT*.

NO, I'M AFRAID I D-- OH.... YES, I DO.

SO, WHO THE HELL ARE *YOU*, KID?

C'MON, OLLIE...

THAT'S *MISTER QUEEN* TO YOU, JUNIOR.

UH... SORRY....

IT'S *ME*, MISTER QUEEN-- *WALLY WEST*.

ROY'S FRIEND? HOLY CATS, LOOK AT THE *SIZE* OF YOU! *C'MERE*, BOY!

MAN, YOU YOUNGSTERS GROW UP *QUICK*! HOW'S ROY? I HAVEN'T BEEN ABLE TO GET IN *TOUCH* WITH HIM, BUT I JUST FIGURED HE WAS ON A *MISSION* WITH YOU AND THE OTHER KIDS. WHAT'RE YOU CALLING YOURSELVES AGAIN...? *JUSTICE LEAGUE JUNIOR...?*

YOU MEAN THE *TEEN TITANS?*

CUTE AS A *BUTTON*! YOU TELL ROY TO CHECK IN WITH HIS *OLD MAN* AS SOON AS HE CAN.

HE'S STAYING OFF THE *HORSE*, ISN'T HE?

UH... AS FAR AS I KNOW, SIR.

GOOD. IT WAS A *CLOSE CALL* THERE FOR A LITTLE BIT, BUT I *KNEW* THE KID WOULD *PULL THROUGH.*

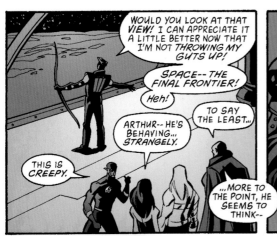

WOULD YOU LOOK AT THAT *VIEW!* I CAN APPRECIATE IT A LITTLE BETTER NOW THAT I'M NOT *THROWING MY GUTS UP!*

SPACE-- THE *FINAL FRONTIER!*

Heh!

ARTHUR-- HE'S BEHAVING... *STRANGELY.*

TO SAY THE *LEAST...*

THIS IS *CREEPY.*

...MORE TO THE POINT, HE SEEMS TO *THINK--*

--IT'S ABOUT *TEN YEARS AGO?*

YEAH! WHAT *GIVES?!*

NO CLUE. HE'S BEEN ACTING LIKE THIS SINCE I *FOUND* HIM TONIGHT. IT'S LIKE HE'S THE OLD OLLIE.

AND I *MEAN* THE *OLD* OLLIE.

BUT HE ACTUALLY LOOKS A BIT *YOUNGER* THAN WHEN I SAW HIM LAST, BACK WHEN HE *KILLED--*

HEY! WHERE'S *HAL* AT, ANYWAY?

WHAT'S WITH THE *LOOKS?* WHAT'D I *SAY?*

OLLIE-- HAL HASN'T BEEN AROUND HERE IN QUITE *AWHILE.* IN FACT, HAL'S--

SORRY I'M LATE. SOME *IDIOT* TRIED TO *BLOW UP* THE TRACKS OF THE *METROPOLIS RAIL-WHALE.*

WHAT DID I--

GREAT CAESAR'S GHOST!

THE MINUTE I GET BACK TO EARTH, I'M HAVING YOUR FUNDING *CUT OFF!*

CONSIDER YOUR CHARTER *REVOKED!*

UHN!

KRAK!

SNIP!

THUD!

WAS THAT *REALLY* NECESSARY?

YOU'D PREFER HE BLEW OUT THE WINDOW?

I WOULD'VE *BEATEN* THAT ARROW...

HOW LONG HAVE YOU BEEN *SKULKING AROUND* HERE?

LONG ENOUGH TO HEAR THAT NONE OF YOU COULD GET PAST YOUR CARTOONISH, SLACK-JAWED *DUMB-FOUNDEDNESS* OVER THE SITUATION AND SECURE ANY *ANSWERS* AS TO WHY A MAN WHO WE ALL *KNOW* IS *DEAD* WALKS AROUND ARTICULATING LIKE A WALKING *ANACHRONISM.*

CATCH.

THAT IS, BY FAR, THE MOST *COMPLEX* SENTENCE I'VE EVER HEARD ANYONE UTTER.

TEN BUCKS SAYS HE'S BEEN HIDING IN THE SHADOWS FOR THE LAST *HOUR*, JUST SO HE COULD COME UP WITH A PUT-DOWN THAT *CLASSY.*

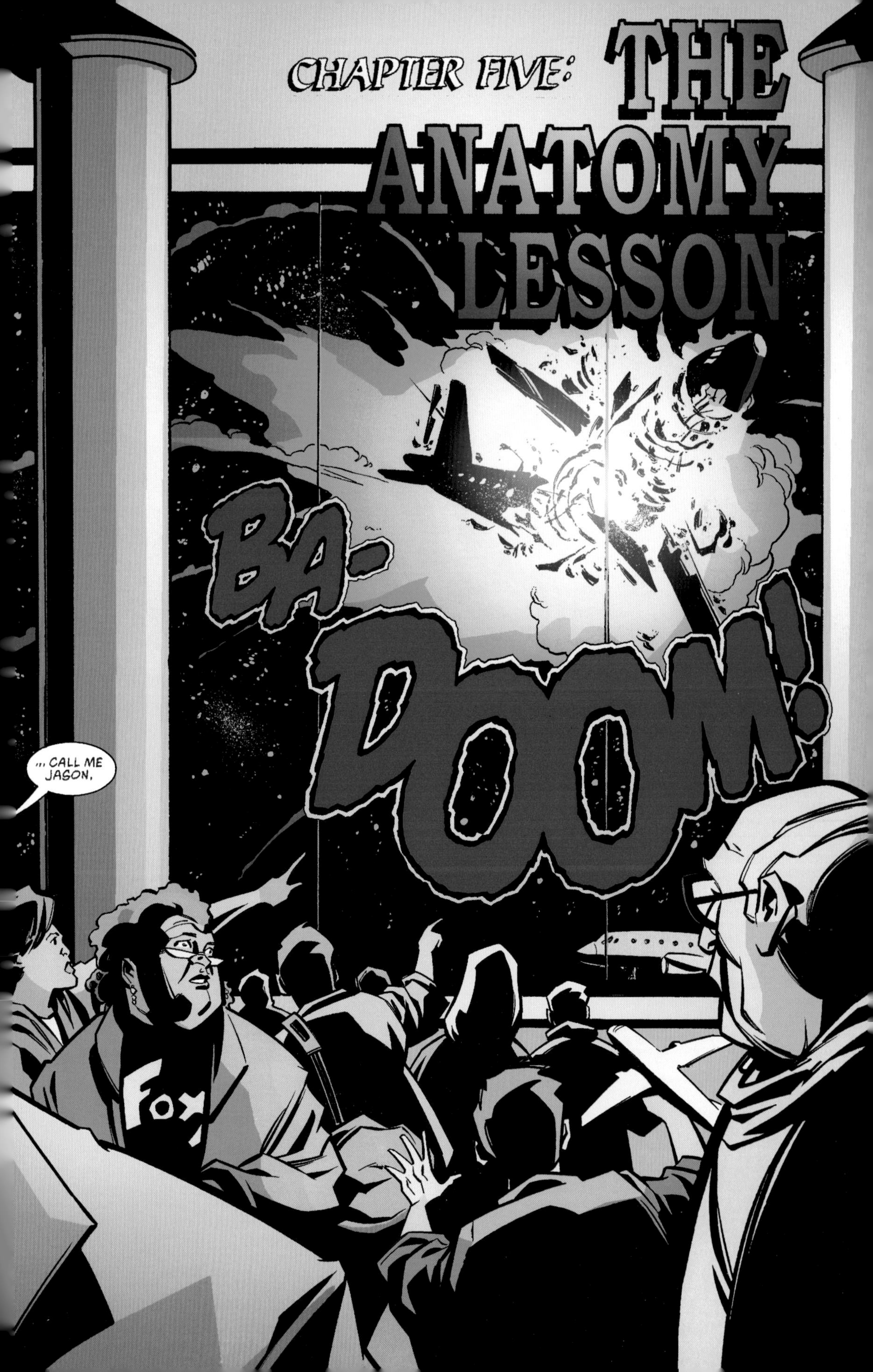
CHAPTER FIVE: THE ANATOMY LESSON
BA-DOOM!
...CALL ME JASON.
FOX

RA'S AL GHUL, NOT 'RASTA-GUY'.

IF I HAD ANY SENSE, I WOULD'VE SENT YOU PACKING WITH ALFRED AND TIM.

IF YOU HAD ANY SENSE, YOU WOULDN'T BE DRESSED LIKE THAT.

ANYWAY...

AND I WAS KEEPING THOSE FILES AS A PRECAUTIONARY MEASURE-- IN CASE ANY OF THEM WENT ROGUE.

Uh-huh.

OLIVER SHOULD HAVE A BYPASS-SURGERY-SIZED SCAR RIGHT HERE.

"THE ASSASSIN SHADO SHOT HIM IN THE CHEST WITH AN ARROW, NARROWLY MISSING HIS HEART. *

"OLIVER ALWAYS MAINTAINED THE MISS WAS INTENTIONAL."

*SEE 'GREEN ARROW' #10

LEMME GUESS-- YOU DON'T AGREE.

FOR ALL HIS CRANKY BLUSTER, OLIVER BELIEVED THAT PEOPLE WERE INHERENTLY GOOD.

I DON'T AFFORD MYSELF THAT OPTIMISTIC LUXURY.

WHICH IS EXACTLY WHY YOU WEREN'T ASKED TO TAKE KATHY LEE'S PLACE BESIDE REGIS.

9

DAILY PLAN...

A HERO FALLS

The masked bowman known as the Green Arrow died in the skies high above Metropolis yesterday, giving his life to save the city from a cataclysmic attack.

While little is known about the tragedy, Superman confirmed the costumed vigilante's demise in an exclusive with the Daily Planet this morning.

The Green Arrow

Crash Site

Oliver Queen

NOW DO YOU SEE THE PROBLEM?

I...

YES, YES, I DO.

THE PROBLEM IS YOU'RE NOT NEARLY AS SMART AS EVERYONE MAKES YOU OUT TO BE, GROOVY-GHOULIE! Ha-ha-ha-ha!

EXCUSE ME?

YOU EXPECT ME TO BELIEVE THAT BUNK?! IT'S A DUMMY PAPER, YOU STOOGE! LOOK AT THAT PICTURE! WHEN HAVE I EVER DRESSED LIKE THAT, MAN?!

Ha-ha-hah!

11

LIKE I REMEMBER WHEN I FOUND OUT ABOUT QUEEN INDUSTRIES' *INVOLVEMENT* IN *WEAPONS MANUFACTURING.* I DECIDED TO *SELL* THE COMPANY SHORTLY AFTER THAT.

THAT WAS AROUND THE TIME WHEN I WAS BECOMING *SOCIALLY CONSCIOUS* AND FEELING *GUILTY* ABOUT BEING WEALTHY, SO I SET UP THE QUEEN FUND, WHICH WAS *SUPPOSED* TO MANAGE THE DISTRIBUTION OF MY FORTUNE OUT TO CHARITIES AND THE POOR.

I WAS BECOMING FAR MORE INTERESTED IN BEING *GREEN ARROW* THAN *OLIVER QUEEN,* SO I LEFT THE DAY-TO-DAY STUFF TO JOHN DELEON.

Star City Examiner
QUEEN A PAWN

MYSTERY ARCHER FOILS BANK JOB

* SEE 'LEGENDS OF THE DCU' # 7-9.

HOW THE HELL WAS *I* SUPPOSED TO KNOW HE WAS GOING TO FRAME ME FOR *EMBEZZLEMENT?*

WHAT I DIDN'T LOSE IN *LITIGATION* AND *FINES,* I JUST WALKED AWAY FROM.

LIKE THE MANSION HERE.

SO WHEN YOU FOUND YOURSELF ON THE STREETS, DRESSED IN RAGS AND UTILIZING A MAKESHIFT ARMORY, WHY DIDN'T YOU JUST COME BACK HERE?

WELL, *LOOK* AT IT! IT'S BORDERING ON *CONDEMNED.* I WAS HAVING IT REBUILT AFTER THE BOMBING INCIDENT AT THE JLA FUNDRAISER WE HELD HERE,* BUT THE MONEY RAN OUT DURING MY LEGAL WOES WITH DELEON.

BESIDES-- I DIDN'T WANT TO HAVE ANYTHING TO *DO* WITH THIS PART OF MY LIFE ANYMORE!

KRSSH

* SEE 'LEGENDS OF THE DCU' #12-13.

THE BRAVE AND THE BOLD #85

The Brave and the Bold #85 (September 1969) struck like a bullet from gun when it first hit the comic book stands. 'The Senator's Been Shot!' screamed the cover headline, perhaps deliberately evoking the Kennedy tragedy of a few years earlier. From the opening page it was clear that this was something different in the world of comics, a taut thriller by writer Bob Haney that looked at the very real-world problems of organised crime and political corruption.

JLA Just as startling was the redesign of Green Arrow by superstar artist Neal Adams. The Emerald Archer now had the appearance of a modern-day Robin Hood. While still a wealthy industrialist, Green Arrow would later lose his fortune, becoming a champion of the people. He developed an anti-establishment persona, always questioning those in power. As a political hothead, Green Arrow was a precursor of the street-level vigilantes and brooding heroes who would dominate comics in the following decades.

JLA In conjunction with writer Dennis O'Neil, Neal Adams developed Green Arrow's character further in Green Lantern/Green Arrow #76-89 (April 1970-May 1972), a widely celebrated run that examined the political differences between the two heroes and tackled controversial social issues such as overpopulation, racism and poverty. A harrowing two-parter, in #85-86, revealed that Green Arrow's teenage partner, Speedy, had succumbed to drug addiction.

JLA The changes to Green Arrow ran deeper than a simple costume makeover. The developments begun in The Brave in the Bold #85 helped humanise Green Arrow. Oliver Queen was presented as a true individual and not just Green Arrow's empty alter ego. Inner torments and conflicts became integral to the character and continued to be important elements of modern-day stories such as

In a groundbreaking run, Green Arrow joined Green Lantern addressed the social ills at the heart of the United States

IF I AM ELECTED... I VOW TO SWEEP OUR STATE AND NATION FREE OF CRIME! TO THIS END, I DEDICATE THE REMAINING YEARS OF MY LIFE...

PAUL'S VOICE... WHAT KIND OF VERMIN WOULD SHOOT A MAN LIKE THAT...

AFTER **BATMAN** RESUMES HIS CIVILIAN IDENTITY, HE GOES DIRECTLY TO GOTHAM STATE HOSPITAL WHERE PAUL CATHCART LIES IN A COMA, BALANCED BETWEEN LIFE AND DEATH. FOR HOURS, BRUCE WAYNE AND THE SENATOR'S SON, EDMOND, STAND SILENT VIGIL AT HIS BEDSIDE...THEN...

MR. WAYNE... IT'S THE **GOVERNOR** CALLING, SIR...

...THANK YOU, NURSE! I'LL BE BACK SHORTLY, EDMOND.

YOU CAN USE THE PHONE IN THE CHIEF RESIDENT'S OFFICE!

BRUCE, THIS IS A TERRIBLE TRAGEDY, BUT PAUL WAS READY FOR IT. I HAVE HIS RESIGNATION FROM THE SENATE HERE, TO GO INTO EFFECT IF HE WERE UNABLE TO VOTE ON HIS ANTI-CRIME BILL. THE DOCTORS SAY HE WON'T BE ABLE TO VOTE. I'M APPOINTING A NEW SENATOR!

PAUL ALWAYS THOUGHT OF HIS VOTERS FIRST. OF COURSE EDMOND WOULD BE **MY** FIRST CHOICE TO REPLACE HIM!

BUT NOT **MINE,** BRUCE. HIS PSYCHIATRIC PRACTICE KEEPS HIM TOO BUSY. EDMOND IS NOT FULLY AWARE OF THE IMPORTANCE OF HIS FATHER'S BILL.

I'M ASKING YOU TO FINISH THE SENATOR'S TERM, BRUCE!

YOU... YOU MUST BE JOKING!

3

THE PROJECT MUST *NOT* GO TO MINOTAUR! LOCK UP THE PLANS BEFORE YOU GO ... WITHOUT THEM OUR BID IS WORTHLESS!

MY OTHER IDENTITY... AS *GREEN ARROW*... I'D ALMOST FORGOTTEN IT! IT'S BEEN SOME TIME... LIKE SOMETHING FROM ANOTHER LIFE... I HAVEN'T EVEN GOTTEN ANY USE OUT OF THIS NEW COSTUME I HAD MADE UP!

AS A FINANCIER, I'M *REALLY* HELPING HUMANITY... ON A BIG SCALE!

THIS MAY BE THE TIME TO DISCARD MY *GREEN ARROW* IDENTITY FOR GOOD!

HMMM, ISN'T THAT WINDOW WASHER WORKING LATE?

WHAT? THEY'RE NOT HERE! MUNSON TOOK THE PLANS!

WHAT'S THAT?... A *GRENADE!!*

GOTTA GET LOW ENOUGH...

THWIIIP

5

YOU WERE RIGHT, BRUCE! THIS WORKOUT IS RELAXING ME. I'VE BEEN UP TIGHT SINCE DAD WAS SHOT. I'M ALSO GLAD THE GOVERNOR APPOINTED YOU TO REPLACE DAD! THAT TAKES ANOTHER LOAD OFF MY MIND!

I'VE BEEN MEANING TO TALK TO YOU ABOUT THAT, EDMOND. I'M AFRAID I CAN'T TAKE THE APPOINTMENT!

CAN'T?? YOU'RE THE ONLY ONE WHO CAN! MY FATHER'S WHOLE CAREER HAS LED UP TO THAT ANTI-CRIME BILL...

YOU MUST!

YOU HAVE THE TIME... THE MONEY... THE KNOWLEDGE! MY FATHER LIES IN A COMA... CLOSE TO DEATH! BATMAN HAS SWORN NOT TO REST UNTIL HE HAS RUN DAD'S ATTACKERS TO THE GROUND...

AND YOU WON'T EVEN STAND UP AND BE COUNTED!

IT'S NOT BECAUSE I DON'T WANT TO, EDMOND...

BUT I GAVE AN OATH TO DO ANOTHER JOB-- BATMAN'S JOB, BECAUSE I AM... BATMAN!

7

BRUCE ... YOU ... *BATMAN?* THIS ISN'T A DODGE ...? NO, IT WOULDN'T BE! BUT WHY ...

WHY TELL *YOU?* TWO REASONS! ONE: YOU *DESERVE* TO KNOW! TWO: I NEED YOUR HELP ... YOUR ADVICE!

AS A PSYCHIATRIST, YOU'LL NEVER REVEAL MY SECRET, SO IT'S SAFE WITH YOU. BUT MY PROBLEM REMAINS.

OF COURSE, WHICH CAREER IS MORE IMPORTANT, SENATOR WAYNE'S OR BATMAN'S? ONE RULES OUT THE OTHER!

IT'S GOT ME TIED IN MENTAL KNOTS!

WITH WHICH CAREER CAN I DO THE MOST GOOD? THE CRIME BILL IS MOST IMPORTANT BUT ...

... WHAT EFFECT WILL THE DISAPPEARANCE OF *BATMAN* HAVE ON CRIME AND CRIMINALS IN GOTHAM ...?

AND ON *BRUCE WAYNE*, WHOSE PERSONALITY IS MOST IMPORTANT IN THIS CASE!

IT'S A DECISION ONLY *YOU* CAN MAKE, BRUCE! ALL I CAN DO IS GUIDE YOU!

YOU'VE ALREADY BEGUN TO CLEAR THE COBWEBS AWAY, ED! THANKS! WILL I SEE YOU AT THE HOSPITAL LATER?

8

THE FOLLOWING MORNING...

...I HEREBY ACCEPT THE OFFICE OF UNITED STATES SENATOR... TO SERVE THE PEOPLE OF THIS STATE...

MINOTAUR MADE UP MY MIND FOR ME! THE ANTI-CRIME BILL MUST PASS!

MEANWHILE ABOVE A SMALL VOLCANIC ISLAND IN THE MEDITERRANEAN...

ED'S ABDUCTION DECIDED ONE THING... I'VE GOT TO PLAY *GREEN ARROW* FOR A WHILE ANYWAY!

SOON...

MINOTAUR'S PRIVATE YACHT... ENTERING A HIDDEN GROTTO!

TO TRAIL THE SLEEK CRAFT WITHIN THE GROTTO'S MAZE, *GREEN ARROW* FIRES AN ELECTRONIC TRACKER SHAFT...

THUNK

BEEP

BEEP BEEP BEEP

12

SO, DR. CATHCART, YOU WILL TELL ME NOTHING OF BRUCE WAYNE AND OLIVER QUEEN?

I'M ONLY THEIR FRIEND, MINOTAUR... I KNOW NOTHING ABOUT THEIR POLITICS OR BUSINESS!

I THINK YOU *LIE!* I HAVE HAD MUCH MORE IMPORTANT MEN THAN YOU KILLED FOR DEFYING ME!

I'LL BET HE HAS... AND MY FATHER MAY YET BE ADDED TO HIS LIST!

A TRACKING DEVICE.. SIR! WE FOUND IT AT THE REAR OF THE SHIP.

SO WE ARE BEING HUNTED! VERY INTERESTING BUT FOOLISH!

WHOEVER HE IS, HE'S NOW ABOUT TO BECOME THE HUNTED! THIS ISLAND IS ALSO MY PRIVATE HUNTING PRESERVE, WELL STOCKED WITH RAVENOUS PREY!

KRUNCH

BLAST! THE SIGNAL'S GONE DEAD! I'M LOST!

13

ARROOOWW
GNRRR
HUFF
SNAP

UH-OH! MINOTAUR'S LET LOOSE SOME PETS!

RAROWW
CHFFF
GNRR

BLAZES! SOUNDS LIKE... THEY'RE COMING...FROM ...EVERYWHERE!

ARROOW
RROW
GRNNN

THWIIIP

GREEN ARROW--!

BATMAN? HOW... HOW IN BLAZES DID YOU FIND ME?

I TRACKED YOUR **JUSTICE LEAGUE** LOCATOR TRANSMITTER! I HOMED IN ON YOU LIKE A PIGEON!

BAD NEWS! BECAUSE I'M A LOST PIGEON, AND NOW THAT MAKES TWO OF US!

I THINK I CAN GET US OUT OF HERE!

BATMAN DOESN'T KNOW THAT AS OLIVER QUEEN MY BID ON "NEW ISLAND" MUST BE SUBMITTED WITHIN 48 HOURS OR MINOTAUR WINS THE CONTRACT BY FORFEIT!

CAN'T TELL HIM I'VE GOT TO BE IN WASHINGTON BY TOMORROW AFTERNOON TO VOTE ON THE ANTI-CRIME BILL!

WHY'D YOU BRING THE BAT DOWN?

IT'S GOING TO LEAD US OUT OF HERE!

SOON...

BATS HAVE THEIR OWN "RADAR" FOR NAVIGATING ANY MAZE--OR NIGHT FLYING--AND WITH ONE OF OUR LOCATOR TRANSMITTERS SENDING SIGNALS BACK TO US...IT'LL LEAD US TO DAYLIGHT...AND MINOTAUR!

KILL YOU--? I AM SIMPLY A BUSINESSMAN! IF YOU'RE JOKING --

I'M NOT, ESPECIALLY WHEN I SAY YOU ARE UNDER ARREST TO BE RETURNED TO AMERICA FOR YOUR CRIMES!

YOU CANNOT ARREST ME HERE IN A FOREIGN COUNTRY!

OH, EXCUSE ME! DIDN'T I MENTION... THIS IS LEGALLY AMERICAN SOIL...? HADN'T YOU NOTICED THIS IS THE **AMERICAN EMBASSY?**

MR. AMBASSADOR! THIS IS AN OUTRAGE!

INDEED, I QUITE AGREE. BUT I'M SURE MR. QUEEN AND THESE FEDERAL MARSHALS WILL BE GLAD TO RETURN YOU HOME WHERE YOU'LL BE CHEERFULLY WELCOMED!

YOU WILL NEVER GET ME TO AN AIRPORT, MR. QUEEN! MY MEN WAIT OUTSIDE!

AH-- BUT I HAVE THE ANSWER FOR **THAT!**

MOMENTS LATER, FROM THE EMBASSY ROOF...

20

AND AS THE CRUCIAL VOTE NEARS A CLOSE

I VOTE... *NO!*

THE BILL'S GOING TO LOSE... UNLESS WAYNE GETS HERE...!

SENATOR BRUCE WAYNE! YOUR VOTE, PLEASE! *SENATOR WAYNE?*

TOO LATE! NO SIGN OF HIM... THE BILL'S LOST!

FOR THE LAST TIME... IS SENATOR WAYNE VOTING ON THIS BILL?

HOPE NOBODY COMES IN -- THERE'S NO SENATOR BATMAN IN CONGRESS -- YET!

SENATOR WAYNE PRESENT AND VOTING, SIR! AND I VOTE... YES!

BRAVO! WE'VE WON!

NOT LONG AFTER IN THE OFFICES OF OLIVER QUEEN...

SO YOU'VE SOLVED YOUR PROBLEM, OLIVER?

YES, ED! "NEW ISLAND" IS SUCCESSFULLY LAUNCHED-- BUT *GREEN ARROW* WAS JUST AS RESPONSIBLE FOR THAT AS I AM! SO I GUESS THERE'S STILL ROOM IN MY LIFE FOR *TWO* IDENTITIES!

AND LATER, AT WAYNE MANOR...

YOU SAY YOU'RE RESIGNING YOUR SENATE SEAT, BRUCE?

THE BILL'S PASSED, ED! AND YOUR FATHER'S ON THE ROAD TO RECOVERY! THE GOVERNOR CAN REAPPOINT HIM TO HIS OLD JOB, A JOB I COULDN'T DO WITHOUT *BATMAN*... SO I'VE MADE MY CHOICE!

EVEN LATER IN HIS OWN OFFICES...

WITH BOTH CONFLICTS RESOLVED, I CAN BEGIN MY AGREED- TO SESSIONS OF SELF- HYPNOSIS TO WIPE THE KNOWLEDGE OF THESE TWO GREAT HEROES' IDENTITIES FROM MY MIND!

The END

23

THE NEXT VOLUME OF THE DC COMICS GRAPHIC NOVEL COLLECTION...

GREEN ARROW

QUIVER
PART 2

DC COMICS™

EAGLEMOSS COLLECTIONS

VOLUME 38

Many questions surround the resurrected Green Arrow. And now, supernatural entities, including Etrigan the Demon, are closing in to bring Oliver Queen's new life to a quick and final end.

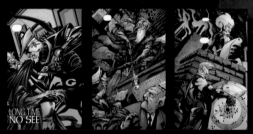

PLUS BLACK CANARY'S FIRST APPEARANCES FROM *FLASH COMICS* #86 & 92

THE FLASH

VOLUME 39

Wally West finds himself caught in the middle of an all-out war between The Flash's greatest enemies, and powerless to end the conflict.

PLUS CAPTAIN COLD'S FIRST APPEARANCE FROM *SHOWCASE* #8

ROGUE WAR

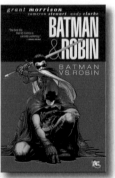

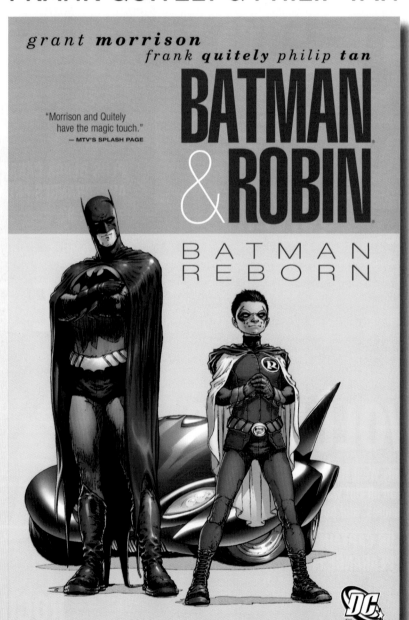